In Own Country

by Margo Simmons
illustrated by Holly M. Jones

Harcourt
SCHOOL PUBLISHERS

Printed in China

ISBN 10: 0-15-351519-8
ISBN 13: 978-0-15-351519-4

Ordering Options
ISBN 10: 0-15-351214-8 (Grade 4 Advanced Collection)
ISBN 13: 978-0-15-351214-8 (Grade 4 Advanced Collection)
ISBN 10: 0-15-358109-3 (package of 5)
ISBN 13: 978-0-15-358109-0 (package of 5)

4 5 6 7 8 9 10 0940 12 11 10 09

Life was good for my family at the start of 1941. Our family business, a small hotel in Los Angeles, was doing well. My brother Joe was ten, and I was twelve, and we were both good students. We were typical American children: we went to school and played with our friends. Joe played baseball, and I took art classes. Our lives were much easier than the lives of our parents had been.

My parents, Kenji and Izumi Natsumi, were born in Japan. When they were in their early twenties, they got married and moved to the United States. They worked at a factory together for several years, lived in a tiny apartment, and saved every penny they earned. Eventually, with the help of a loan from a bank, they purchased the hotel.

We had a small, but comfortable, home in Los Angeles. My father was at the hotel a lot, working hard to keep the customers happy, while my mom took care of the work at home. Joe and I enjoyed spending time at the hotel. We would help my father out in any way we could, and we enjoyed meeting the many people who stayed there.

Our lives changed forever, though, on December 7, 1941. Joe and I were out in front of our house playing catch.

"Sue, you and Joe must come inside immediately!" my mother exclaimed, running out of the house.

"What's wrong?" I asked as we hurried inside and sat down in the front room.

The newsperson on the radio was talking about a military attack at Pearl Harbor, in Hawaii. This was the place where the United States Navy had many of its ships. "The United States has been attacked by the Japanese," my mother explained. Joe and I looked at each other and cringed, not sure what to think.

A moment later the phone rang. It was my father, and I overheard my mother talking and crying. We stayed in the house the rest of the day, listening to the radio and worrying about the situation.

Joe and I walked to school the next morning as usual. We ran into one of Joe's friends, and he averted his eyes. "My mom says I can't play with you anymore," he said shyly.

Joe was confused and did not understand why this was happening. I thought to myself, "That must be because of the Japanese bombing the ships. How can Joe's mom think we had anything to do with that? How could she accuse us of that? We're Americans—we were born here and lived here our whole lives."

A moment later, though, my good friend Jenny walked up and said hi. She was the same Jenny I had always known: friendly and kind. It felt so good to be treated normally!

Before long the United States entered World War II, fighting against Germany and Japan. Everyone was nervous and upset about the war. Some people treated my family badly.

Sometimes when I am upset, I write poems that tell how I feel to make myself feel better:

I was sad when I heard the ships were hit
and upset when the people were hurt.
I love my country and want it to be fine
because I'm an American more than anything.

Things are different now.
People don't look at me the same way.
I wish it could go back to how it was,
enjoying my friends and neighborhood.

7

In March 1942, my mother gave us some horrible news: The United States was forcing all Japanese-Americans in California, Oregon, and Washington out of their homes. The government was worried that Japan was going to attack the West Coast of the United States and that Japanese people living here would help them.

"Where are we supposed to go?" I asked.

"I'm not sure," she replied.

"How long will we be gone?" Joe wanted to know.

"No one knows," Mother responded sadly.

She and my father discussed the situation with other Japanese friends to try to find out what was happening. They learned that there would be ten camps set up for Japanese people. We had only a few weeks to leave our homes and report to one of them.

Over the next three weeks, we sold most of our belongings. Father was forced to sell the hotel for an incredibly low price, and we sold our car, furniture, books, and house. Our neighbor, Mrs. Daniels, let us store some things in her basement, but for the most part, all we kept was some clothing to wear at the camp. I had never cried so much in my entire life. My nice life was quickly becoming awful, and I worried that the worst was yet to come.

In late March, we solemnly boarded a train to eastern California. We were assigned to the camp called Manzanar.

When we arrived at Manzanar, we were searched and interrogated. They must have asked us a thousand questions. Then we were given a tiny apartment that had small mattresses filled with straw. My father was in a fury, but he just sat down with a stern look on his face and said nothing.

A barbed-wire fence surrounded the entire camp. There were armed guards all around. Over ten thousand Japanese people were at the camp, all of them living in small, cramped little apartments—and all of them wondering why they were forced to live like this *in their own country*. The only thing that made the camp livable was that there were those thousands of other people there, just like us.

That night I wrote a poem to make myself feel
a little better:

All the joy in my heart has left.
I spend my days feeling sad,
wondering if I will ever be happy again.
The days go by, and my heart is heavy.

I wish I could see my friends,
talk with them, joke around, and laugh.
I want to be back in my bedroom,
drawing and sketching the way I used to.

When will I see my aunts and uncles?
How are my cousins doing now?
Are their hearts heavy and sad like mine?
Are they lonely and cold like me?

The months passed, and we managed all right.
It always made me sad, though, to see those little
Japanese boys and girls—just five, six, seven years
old—being forced to live in this odd camp.

By the spring of 1944, the Americans were winning
the war, and the Japanese were no longer considered
a threat to the United States. At the start of 1945, the
United States government announced that, by the end
of the year, the camps would be closed, and all Japanese
people would be free to go.

Our happiness was mixed with worry. What would
it be like when we went back? How would other
Americans treat us? Since we had lost our house and
hotel and property, where would we live and what
would we do?

In April 1945, we finally left Manzanar. As we drove from the camp to the train station, I craned my neck to look back at the strange place that was our "home" for three years. We had written our neighbor, Mrs. Daniels, and she came to pick us up when we got off the train in Los Angeles. We drove toward Long Beach, where my uncle lived. He had been in a camp, too, but one of his neighbors had offered to watch his house, so my uncle still owned it when he was released. My family was going to stay there until we got settled in our new lives.

On our way there, Joe asked, "Mrs. Daniels, will you drive us by our old house?" My mother and father looked at each other with strange looks. It seemed like they wanted to see the house, but that they also *didn't* want to see it. Then my father nodded to Mrs. Daniels, and we drove there.

Everything on our street looked exactly the same. We had sold the house to an older couple, and Mrs. Daniels said they had taken good care of it. Still, none of us could keep from feeling sad when we finally drove past it. I also felt anger since my parents had worked so hard for that house, and they had lost it just because we were Japanese-Americans.

For a while it was hard getting back to our old lives, but eventually life settled back to normal, at least a new normal. We would never forget our experience, but we had survived, and we were still all together.

Think Critically

1. How was the family's life in the camp different from how it was in Los Angeles?

2. What are the two main settings in this story?

3. Why were many Japanese-Americans placed in camps during World War II?

4. How did Sue feel when she heard her family had to move to a camp?

5. What are some details from this story that interested you?

 Social Studies

Map Study Sue and Joe's family were from Japan originally. Japan is in Asia. Find Japan on a map. List some interesting things you notice about Japan on the map.

School-Home Connection Share with a family member what you learned from this story. Then have a discussion about how you would handle a difficult situation like the family in this story went through.

Word Count: 1,441